My Baptism Day

(Picture of me)

DESERET
BOOK

Salt Lake City, UT

Citation credits

Page 18: *Discourses of President Gordon B. Hinckley, Vol. 1, 1995–1999* (Salt Lake City: Deseret Book, 2005), 333.

Page 20: *The Teachings of Ezra Taft Benson* (Salt Lake City: Deseret Book, 1988), 349.

Page 25: "The Great Symbol of Our Membership," *Ensign,* October 1994, 5.

Page 26: *Teachings of Thomas S. Monson* (Salt Lake City: Deseret Book, 2011), 154.

Page 42: "Be Thou an Example," *Ensign,* May 2015, 115.

Illustrations by Zach Clough. http://zachclough.blogspot.com

Cover and background illustration: AmandaKremser/Shutterstock

Design: Shauna Gibby

Book Design © Deseret Book Company

Visit us at DeseretBook.com

ISBN 978-1-62972-269-6
Printed on acid-free paper

Printed in China   03/2018
RR Donnelley, Shenzhen, Guangdong, China
10   9   8   7   6   5   4   3

"Come unto me, and believe in my gospel, and be baptized in my name."

—Ether 4:18

I Am Unique!

There is no one
in the world like me.
I am important to Heavenly
Father and He loves me.
He knows all of the things that
make me special because
I am His child.

Some Things That Make Me Unique

My full name is _____

I was born in _____

I live in _____

I go to school at _____

My favorite subject is _____

I love to _____

Here is a list of people in my family _____

_____

My favorite activity is _____

If I could pick anything I wanted for dinner it would be

_____

If I could have any super power it would be _____

Because Heavenly Father loves me,
he wants me to return to Him someday. He sent His Son
to be our example and show us the way.

"And it came to pass in those days, that Jesus came from Nazareth of Galilee, and was baptized of John in Jordan. And straightway coming up out of the water, he saw the heavens opened, and the Spirit like a dove descending upon him: and there came a voice from heaven, saying, Thou art my beloved Son, in whom I am well pleased."

—Mark 1:9–11

I followed Jesus's example
and was baptized on

_____

I was baptized by _____

I was confirmed by _____

My bishop's name was _____

My ward was the _____

In the _____ stake

My Primary teacher was _____

The speakers were _____

_____

The song I liked best was _____

Something I remember the speaker saying is _____

_____

How I felt when I stepped in the water _____

_____

How I felt after I was baptized _____

_____

_____

Something I remember about being confirmed _____

_____

Some things that were said in my confirmation blessing

_____

_____

What I remember about the rest of the day _____

_____

_____

_____

Guest Sign-in

Guest Sign-in

Guest Sign-in

_____

_____

_____

_____

_____

_____

_____

_____

Guest Sign-in

When I Am Baptized, I Promise:

To take Jesus Christ's name upon me

by becoming a member of His Church

To remember the Savior and think of Him often

To obey the commandments and follow Jesus's example

When I Am Baptized, the Lord Promises:

To give me the gift of the Holy Ghost

To forgive my sins when I repent

To bring me home to be with Him again someday

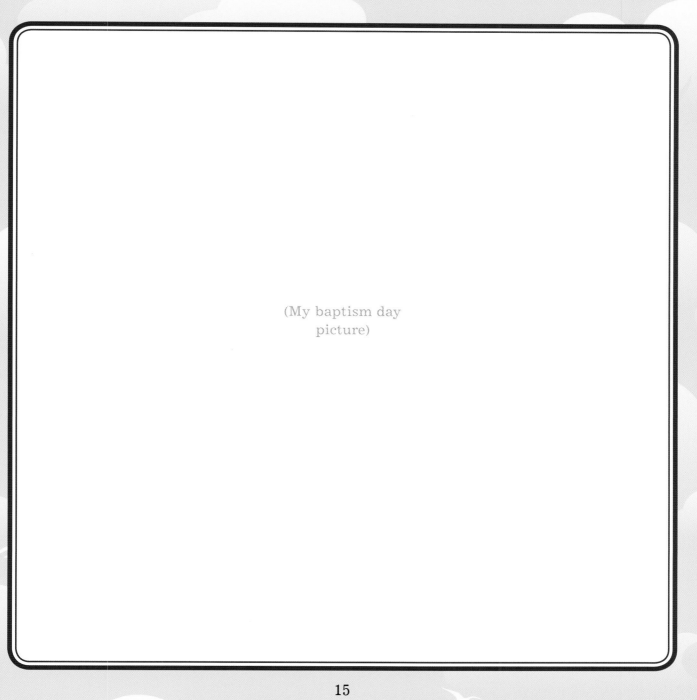

(My baptism day
picture)

The Holy Ghost can teach me
To recognize what's true.
The Holy Ghost can guide me
And show me what to do.
The Holy Ghost can warn me
And keep me safe from harm.
The Holy Ghost can comfort me
So I feel safe and warm.

"Every time we partake of the sacrament, we renew that covenant, we take upon ourselves the name of Jesus Christ and contract, as it were, with Him to keep His commandments. He in turn says that His spirit will be with us. That is a covenant, a two-party contract."

—Gordon B. Hinckley

"You are learning now to keep all the commandments of the Lord. As you do so, you will have His Spirit to be with you. You will feel good about yourselves."

—Ezra Taft Benson

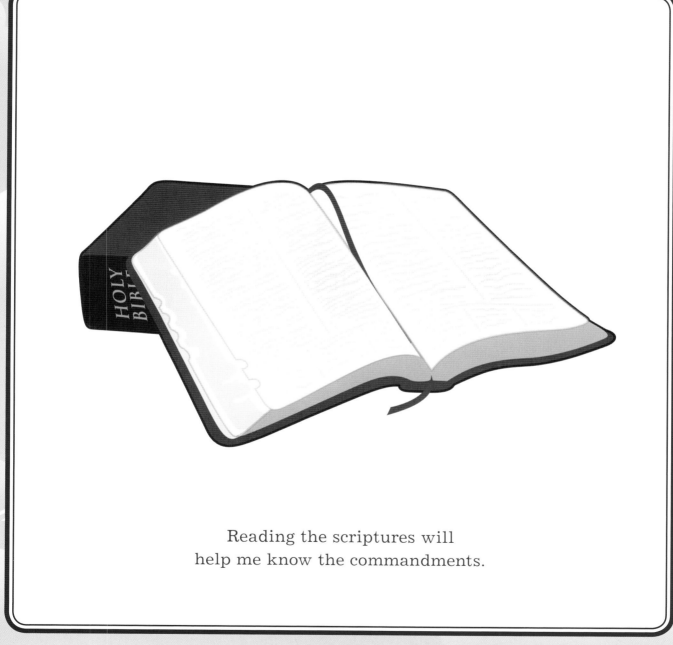

Reading the scriptures will
help me know the commandments.

When I make mistakes I can repent.

"But as oft as they repented and sought forgiveness, with real intent, they were forgiven."

—Moroni 6:8

Baptism is the first covenant I have made with
Heavenly Father. I will try to live the commandments so
that one day I can make covenants in the temple too.

"The temple is a place of beauty,
it is a place of revelation,
it is a place of peace."

—Howard W. Hunter

"Our Lord and Savior,
Jesus Christ, is our Exemplar
and our strength. He is the light
that shineth in darkness. He is
the Good Shepherd."

—Thomas S. Monson

Now that I have followed Jesus Christ's example and
been baptized and confirmed, I am a member of His church.
These are the things we believe:

Articles of Faith

1 We believe in God, the Eternal Father, and in His Son, Jesus Christ, and in the Holy Ghost.

2 We believe that men will be punished for their own sins, and not for Adam's transgression.

3 We believe that through the Atonement of Christ, all mankind may be saved, by obedience to the laws and ordinances of the Gospel.

4 We believe that the first principles and ordinances of the Gospel are: first, Faith in the Lord Jesus Christ; second, Repentance; third, Baptism by immersion for the remission of sins; fourth, Laying on of hands for the gift of the Holy Ghost.

5 We believe that a man must be called of God, by prophecy, and by the laying on of hands by those who are in authority, to preach the Gospel and administer in the ordinances thereof.

6 We believe in the same organization that existed in the Primitive Church, namely, apostles, prophets, pastors, teachers, evangelists, and so forth.

7 We believe in the gift of tongues, prophecy, revelation, visions, healing, interpretation of tongues, and so forth.

8 We believe the Bible to be the word of God as far as it is translated correctly; we also believe the Book of Mormon to be the word of God.

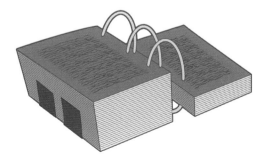

9 We believe all that God has revealed, all that He does now reveal, and we believe that He will yet reveal many great and important things pertaining to the Kingdom of God.

10 We believe in the literal gathering of Israel and in the restoration of the Ten Tribes; that Zion (the New Jerusalem) will be built upon the American continent; that Christ will reign personally upon the earth; and, that the earth will be renewed and receive its paradisiacal glory.

11 We claim the privilege of worshiping Almighty God according to the dictates of our own conscience, and allow all men the same privilege, let them worship how, where, or what they may.

12 We believe in being subject to kings, presidents, rulers, and magistrates, in obeying, honoring, and sustaining the law.

13 We believe in being honest, true, chaste, benevolent, virtuous, and in doing good to all men; indeed, we may say that we follow the admonition of Paul—We believe all things, we hope all things, we have endured many things, and hope to be able to endure all things. If there is anything virtuous, lovely, or of good report or praiseworthy, we seek after these things.

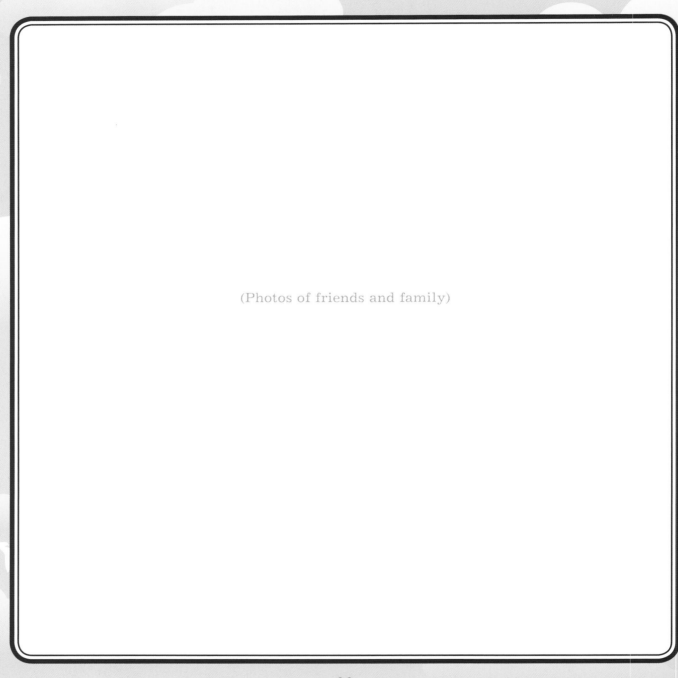

(Photos of friends and family)

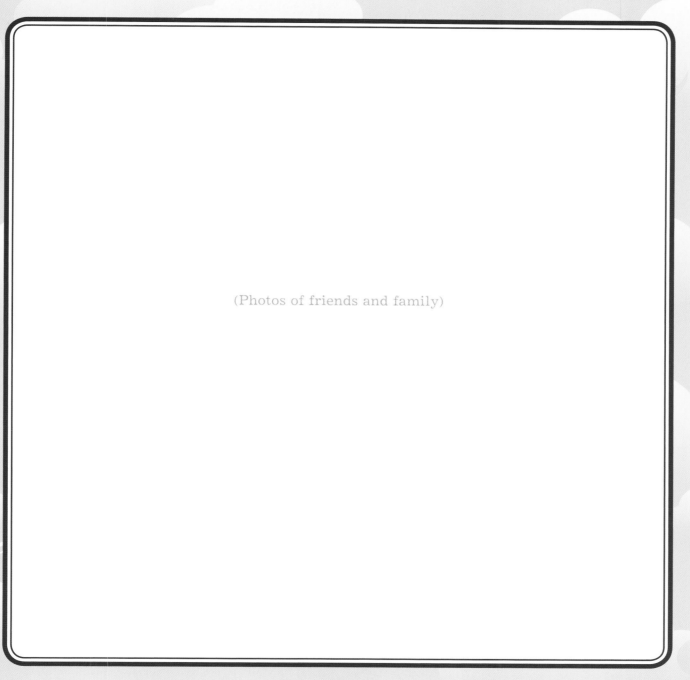

(Photos of friends and family)

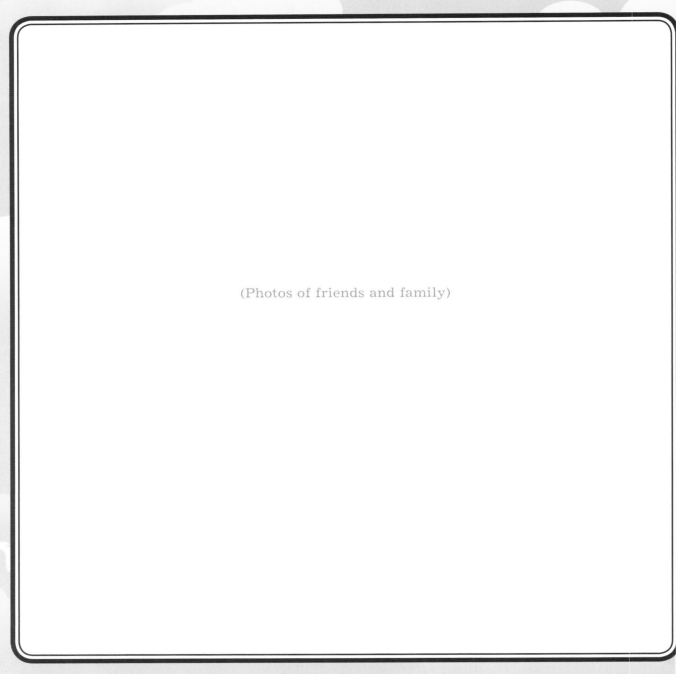

(Photos of friends and family)

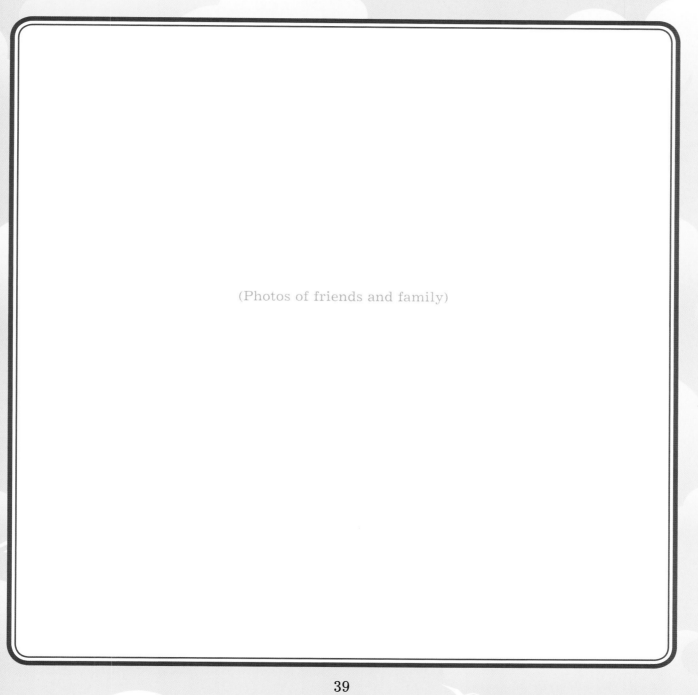

(Photos of friends and family)

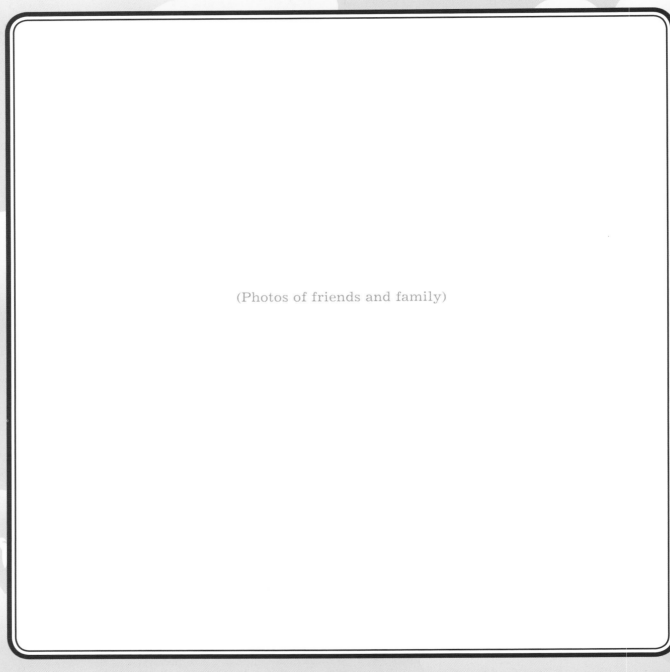

(Photos of friends and family)

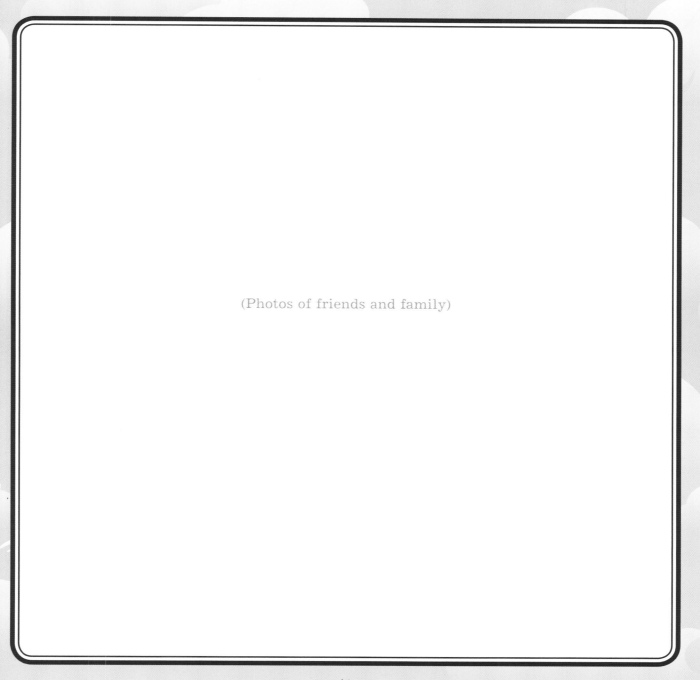

(Photos of friends and family)

"Never underestimate
the far-reaching influence
of your testimony."

—Thomas S. Monson

Sharing testimonies can help faith stay strong.
Here are some testimonies of my family and friends.

Testimonies of My Family and Friends

Testimonies of My Family and Friends

Testimonies of My Family and Friends

Testimonies of My Family and Friends

Testimonies of My Family and Friends

My Testimony

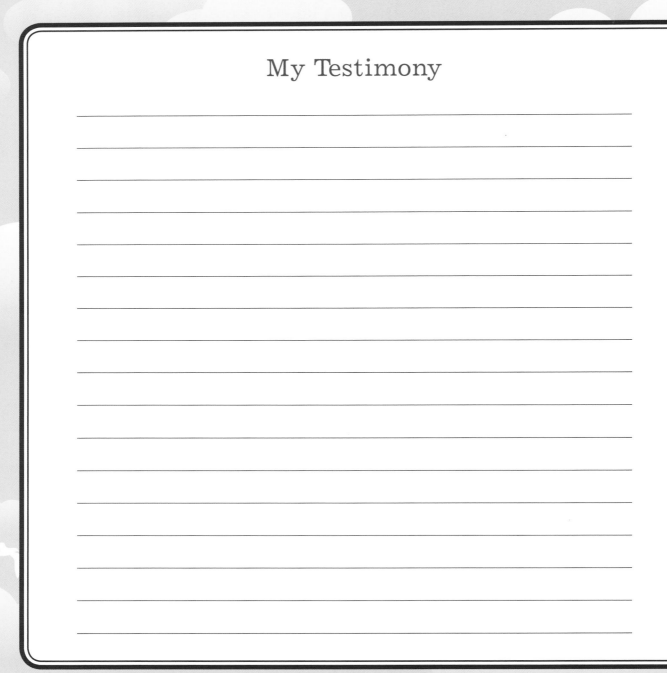

My Testimony